For Leroy and Olive – LS

A special thanks to Catherine for all her help making Nat and Mr Paws as naughty as possible.

Scholastic Children's Books,
Euston House, 24 Eversholt Street,
London NW1 1DB, UK

A division of Scholastic Ltd
London ~ New York ~ Toronto ~ Sydney ~ Auckland
Mexico City ~ New Delhi ~ Hong Kong

First published in Australia by Scholastic Australia, 2013
Published in the UK by Scholastic Ltd, 2014

Text and illustrations © Louis Shea, 2013

ISBN 978 1407 15535 7

Printed and bound by Tien Wah Press, Pte, Ltd, Malaysia

2 4 6 8 10 9 7 5 3 1

WHERE'S SANTA?
AROUND THE WORLD

NOW with over **800** things to spot!

LOUIS SHEA

SCHOLASTIC

AFTER ANOTHER BUSY CHRISTMAS, SANTA AND MRS CLAUS ARE HEADING OFF ON A WELL-DESERVED HOLIDAY. THE SLEIGH IS PACKED (WITH A COUPLE OF UNEXPECTED PASSENGERS) AND EVERYONE WAVES GOODBYE.

DECIDING TO GIVE THE REINDEERS A BREAK, SANTA AND MRS CLAUS JOIN THE PASSENGERS ON BOARD *THE MERRY SEA STAR* FOR A RELAXING CRUISE— WHAT BETTER WAY TO SEE THE WORLD!

Naughty, nice, nice, nice, naughty . . .

Oh, Mr Claus! Can't you stop working for a moment? Put your list away at once, and have a rest!

Yes, dear. Sorry, ho, ho, ho.

Isn't it lovely to have a break? Very relaxing this.

MEANWHILE, UNBEKNOWNST TO SANTA AND MRS CLAUS, NAUGHTY NAT, THE WORLD'S NAUGHTIEST CHILD, HAS OVERHEARD EVERYTHING AND IS PLOTTING A DEVIOUS PLAN . . .

Well, Mr Claus, we meet at last. That pony I was expecting at Christmas never turned up. All I got was a jigsaw puzzle!

MUAHAHAHAHA

Well, that's not going to happen again this year! I will get that list and put my name on the NICE side! Then the pony will be all mine.

SOMETIME LATER, SANTA IS PARTAKING IN HIS FAVOURITE HOLIDAY PASTIME . . .

Excuse me, Sir. I think you dropped this.

Thank you, Nicholas. You're being a very good boy again this year, ho, ho, ho.

Oh no! Foiled by that goodie-goodie, Nick! That list WILL be mine, no matter what. Come, Mr Paws, we have work to do.

PURRRRRR

It's not only Santa travelling around the world! Can you find each of these hidden at every stop?

Santa ✓

After a busy Christmas making and delivering all those toys, Santa really deserves a rest! Dressed in his finest holiday attire, he is off on a relaxing holiday cruise, eager to see the wonders of the world. Can you find where he goes?

Mrs Claus ✓

Mrs Claus has been planning this trip for a long time! She has booked the tickets, packed the bags and given all the elves jobs to do around the house. She even picked up a brand-new holiday outfit!

Naughty Nat ✓

Still fuming about the jigsaw she received last Christmas, Naughty Nat is out to even the score! She is following Santa to steal his list and write her name on the NICE side, so she will get her pony. See if you can find where she's lurking.

Mr Paws ✓

Mr Paws is Naughty Nat's pet cat. But don't be fooled by his cuddly coat and cute kitty looks, he is there to help Nat steal Santa's naughty-and-nice list—unless he gets distracted by a ball of wool to chase!

Mr and Mrs Goode ✓

Poor Mr and Mrs Goode! Naughty Nat's patient parents are now travelling around the world too. But there'll be no sightseeing for them! No, they need to convince their little princess to come home (and leave Santa alone).

Pink Pony

Naughty Nat was expecting this fine filly to arrive in her stocking last Christmas. But Pink Pony presents only come to those who are nice, not naughty! Can you find where the pony is now?

Nice Nick ✓

Nick is on holiday with his family to celebrate yet another year of good grades and perfect behaviour. He has already helped Santa find his list once. See if Santa will need Nick's help again!

Elvy ✓

Elvy is one of Santa's cleverest and hardest-working elves. So when he heard Santa was off on a relaxing vacation, he decided he should come along as well—without telling Santa, of course!

Fluffy ✓

Santa's beloved pet yeti, Fluffy, just couldn't bear to be left behind in the North Pole while Santa and Mrs Claus are away. Not known for doing as he's told, Fluffy stowed away in the sleigh and is enjoying the trip!

Santa's naughty-and-nice list ✓

Santa can sometimes be a bit forgetful, and loses things quite easily! Help him find his naughty-and-nice list, and make sure this magic checklist doesn't end up in the hands of Naughty Nat.

Suitcase ✓

Before departing the North Pole, Mrs Claus and Santa packed their suitcase very carefully—and checked it twice! Help them keep an eye on their luggage so they don't leave it behind anywhere.

Globe ✓

And the next stop is...? Santa and Mrs Claus have this globe of the world with them, to keep track of where they are. Make sure you find where it is, or they might get lost and not make it back to the North Pole!

Mrs Claus' knitting ✓

It gets a bit nippy out in the sleigh at night when delivering all those presents. So Mrs Claus is knitting a lovely Christmas scarf for Santa to help keep him warm and cosy on his busiest night of the year.

LATER THAT NIGHT . . .

The reindeer should be here to take us home very soon.

I'll just check again we have everything packed.

Let's see, suitcase . . . check. Knitting . . . check. Globe . . . check.

Stop that, Elvy! List . . . now, where has that got to?

AT LAST! THE LIST IS MINE!

Ah, there it is!

Thank you for finding it for me, Natalie. That's very **good** of you.

Look, the reindeer are here!

Santa has been quite the tourist on his around-the-world holiday! See if you can find all these wacky and wonderful things that he has seen at each stop along the way.

The Merry Sea Star

- [ ] 12 Crabs
- [ ] 11 Pelicans
- [ ] 10 Sunscreen bottles
- [ ] 9 Snorkelling masks
- [ ] 8 Sombreros
- [ ] 7 Beach balls
- [ ] 6 Life jackets
- [ ] 5 Waiters
- [ ] 4 Telescopes
- [ ] 3 Fishing rods
- [ ] 2 Anchors
- [ ] 1 Blackbeard the pirate

The Great Barrier Reef

- [ ] 12 Dolphins
- [ ] 11 Mermaids
- [ ] 10 Santa squids
- [ ] 9 Clownfish
- [ ] 8 Koalas
- [ ] 7 Treasure chests
- [ ] 6 Green turtles
- [ ] 5 Christmas box jellyfish
- [ ] 4 Seahorses
- [ ] 3 Messages in a bottle
- [ ] 2 Rubber duckies
- [ ] 1 Poseidon, God of the Sea

Great Wall of China

- [ ] 12 Pigs
- [ ] 11 Dogs
- [ ] 10 Roosters
- [ ] 9 Monkeys
- [ ] 8 Goats
- [ ] 7 Horses
- [ ] 6 Snakes
- [ ] 5 Dragons
- [ ] 4 Rabbits
- [ ] 3 Tigers
- [ ] 2 Oxen
- [ ] 1 Rat

Egypt

- [ ] 12 Aliens
- [ ] 11 Santa sphinxes
- [ ] 10 Christmas mummies
- [ ] 9 Scorpions
- [ ] 8 Crocodiles
- [ ] 7 Scarab beetles
- [ ] 6 Canopic jars
- [ ] 5 Camels
- [ ] 4 Ankhs
- [ ] 3 Crowns of Egypt
- [ ] 2 Sceptres
- [ ] 1 Tutankhamen

Oh, deer! Santa's still on holiday? Then I'm coming too! Find me in every scene.

Stonehenge

- [ ] 12 Gnomes
- [ ] 11 Fish and chips
- [ ] 10 Toads
- [ ] 9 Ghost knights
- [ ] 8 Pixies
- [ ] 7 Cauldrons
- [ ] 6 Hobgoblins
- [ ] 5 Foxes
- [ ] 4 Trolls
- [ ] 3 Swords in the stone
- [ ] 2 Fawns
- [ ] 1 Holy Grail

The Alps

- [ ] 12 Saint Bernards
- [ ] 11 Skiing snowmen
- [ ] 10 Alpine marmots
- [ ] 9 Alphorns
- [ ] 8 Alpine ibex
- [ ] 7 Chocolate bars
- [ ] 6 Cowbells
- [ ] 5 Cheese wheels
- [ ] 4 Fondue sets
- [ ] 3 Bobsleds
- [ ] 2 Lederhosen
- [ ] 1 Jack Frost

Paris

- [ ] 12 Mime artists
- [ ] 11 Snails
- [ ] 10 French poodles
- [ ] 9 Baguettes
- [ ] 8 Gargoyles
- [ ] 7 Artist's palettes
- [ ] 6 Chocolate eclairs
- [ ] 5 Unicycles
- [ ] 4 Unique statues of Santa
- [ ] 3 Musketeers
- [ ] 2 Accordions
- [ ] 1 Quasimodo

Canada

- [ ] 12 Grizzly bears
- [ ] 11 Mounties
- [ ] 10 Beavers
- [ ] 9 Maple leaves
- [ ] 8 Moose
- [ ] 7 Hot dogs
- [ ] 6 Bottles of maple syrup
- [ ] 5 Broken hockey sticks
- [ ] 4 Mouth guards
- [ ] 3 Snowmobiles
- [ ] 2 Santa totems
- [ ] 1 Big Foot

New York

- [ ] 12 People wearing rat costumes
- [ ] 11 Alligators
- [ ] 10 Apples
- [ ] 9 Baseballs
- [ ] 8 Pretzels
- [ ] 7 Tickets
- [ ] 6 Squirrels
- [ ] 5 Slices of pizza
- [ ] 4 Theatre ushers
- [ ] 3 People with broken legs
- [ ] 2 Fire hydrants
- [ ] 1 Phantom of the opera